PUFFIN BOOKS

Two's Company

Jackie Kay is a highly original poet and playwright, who has also written for television and radio. She is popular for readings of her work in this country, and has also given readings in North America, where her play *Twice Over* has been performed. Although she now lives and works in London, her childhood was spent in Scotland, and this has become the inspiration for many of her poems.

Two's Company

Jackie Kay

Illustrated by
Shirley Tourret

PUFFIN BOOKS

For Matthew and Maxine

PUFFIN BOOKS

Published by the Penguin Group
Penguin Books Ltd, 27 Wrights Lane, London W8 5TZ, England
Penguin Books USA Inc., 375 Hudson Street, New York, New York 10014, USA
Penguin Books Australia Ltd, Ringwood, Victoria, Australia
Penguin Books Canada Ltd, 10 Alcorn Avenue, Toronto, Ontario, Canada M4V 3B2
Penguin Books (NZ) Ltd, 182–190 Wairau Road, Auckland 10, New Zealand

Penguin Books Ltd, Registered Offices: Harmondsworth, Middlesex, England

First published by Blackie 1992
Published in Puffin Books 1994
1 3 5 7 9 10 8 6 4 2

Filmset in 12/15 Linotype Palatino

Printed in England by Clays Ltd, St Ives plc

Contents

Introduction

When I was working with Jackie Kay towards the publication of *Two's Company* I often telephoned her. Sometimes her son, Matthew (now aged 3½) would be on the answerphone, telling callers about his idol Michael Jackson, and singing part of a song. Matthew, a highly original boy, appears in some of his mother's poems, and his questions, ideas and sayings have often been an inspiration to her.

The bond between these two is very strong, and Jackie Kay's relationship with her own parents is equally firm. They adopted her as a baby, and she grew up in the 1960's and 1970's in a busy outgoing, lively Glasgow home. Her parents were members of the Communist Party and when Jackie was older she helped her father with canvassing at election times.

Poetry was introduced into Jackie's life when she was quite young, through the popular annual event in Scotland: the Burns Supper, on January 25th. This celebrates the life of Scotland's great poet Robert Burns, and Jackie especially remembers:

'big trestle tables, with white tablecloths, all laid out like a banquet in a story . . . it was like going into another world, a world that you could imagine looking at through a window . . . magical, somehow, and yet . . . there I was, a part of it all . . .'

The way she told me about Burns Night really excited me, and I said at once 'You could write a poem about that'. To my great pleasure, she did, and as you'll see it's in this collection, vividly bringing to life Jackie as a wee girl, caught up in the magic and music of this special occasion.

Some of the first poems Jackie came across were by Robert Burns. There was 'To a Mouse', which begins 'wee sleekit cowrin', tim'rous beastie', the dramatic 'Tam o' Shanter' and one she learnt by heart, 'To a Louse', an amusing poem about a louse on a lady's hat in church . . .

> 'Ye ugly creepin', blasted wonner,
> Detested, shunned by saunt an' sinner,
> How daur ye set your fit upon her—
> Sae fine a lady?
> Gat somewhere else, and seek your dinner
> On some poor body'.

The sounds and beats attracted her, but she didn't think of writing poems herself until she was 12. Her first attempt was actually published in The Morning Star:

> 'We lived in a tenement
> Which was somewhat dreich
> It was damp and dirty and much too small . . .
> But despite all of these things
> We managed to live
> And trusted in yin anither
> For love was the biggest factor of all
> And it kept us all thegither—

'Dreich' means 'dreary', 'yin anither'—'one another', 'thegither'—'together'. Some of the Scots dialect words Jackie uses are easy to guess, but we've given you the clues to the trickier ones in this book.

Jackie Kay's first collection of poems for young people is not lightly called *Two's Company*: she likes the idea of twos, pairs, and doubles. In many poems you will meet the intriguing character Carla Johnson for whom the figure 2 is equally important. Carla's parents are separated, so she knows two houses, two ways of life, two sets of possessions. This can be both rewarding and annoying, particularly when belongings get left in the wrong place. But Carla is even more unusual, because of her imaginary friend, the highly individual OTHER Carla, the special person in her life, who is always there when needed. Carla has many talents and even runs her own Skelf Helpline, for those unlucky children who need a splinter—or skelf, the Scottish word for this—removed.

In Jackie's own childhood her imaginary friend was Brendon Gallacher and he's the subject of another poem. Much less agreeable was the real-life bully, Duncan McKay (not his real name) a boy at her primary school, who made play-times an anxiety. She was much happier at her secondary school, where for the first time she could enjoy subjects taught individually, and found she was not merely 'average' but good at English, Languages and History.

After school, she read English at Stirling University and wrote poetry that no-one saw, morbid and inward-looking. Then Artrage, a multi-cultural arts magazine published her work and she was encouraged to go on. When Jackie moved to London, she gained experience from a mixture of interesting jobs, all of which she has drawn on in her writing. She worked in a Children's Centre; for Sheba, the feminist publisher; as a porter at Westminster Hospital; and then in 1991 was Writer-in-Residence at Shepherds Bush Library. This job was particularly inspiring, working with local poets, the unemployed, sick people and schools; arranging events and running adult literacy classes. The ideas she initiated continue in Hammersmith.

Jackie's love of drama—as a child she wanted to be an actress and went to classes at the Royal Scottish Academy of Music and Drama—has never left her. She is extremely gifted at reading her poetry aloud. Her style is individual, she is sharp, vital and expressive: the audience sits up and listens. It is this interest in drama that gives her such strong visual ideas, and such a fine ear for dialogue and character. She also writes for theatre, television and radio. Her first play *Chiaroscuro* was presented by the Theatre of Black Women in 1986, her second *Twice Over* (note the title!) by Gay Sweatshop in 1988. She has scripted TV films on the subjects of Aids and Trans-racial adoption, and in 1992 a poetry documentary based on a true murder case. *Twice Through The Heart*, for BBC 2.

Every year the Gregory Awards are given to writers under the age of 30, and in 1991, with the publication of her highly acclaimed adult poetry collection, *The Adoption Papers*, Jackie was one of those winners. She is a poet of perception, depth of understanding, emotion and humour; and none of these qualities are in any way watered down in her approach to a younger readership.

ANNE HARVEY

Two Carla Johnsons

People don't understand: there are two Carla
  Johnsons.
The one with wings and the one with hands.
The one who flies and the one who flops exams.
The one who goes to Alaska, to Alabama.
And the one who lives in a high-rise tower.

Two Carlas: one whose wings are sugar paper.
One whose stomach sticks out from a hernia.
One soars through rainbows; one looks out windows.
One who constantly dreams of the other Carla
who has a nicer nose better clothes and good hair.

Good hair that changes colour with temper.
So if she is sad it is blue, if she is happy
it is black, if she is mad it is bright red.
Two Carlas; the one who talks a strange tongue
that nobody but the other Carla can understand.

Often Carla sits in her tower laughing at jokes.
Till the stars fall down. Till the trees dance.
Till her curtains open and close themselves.
All because the one with the wings is so funny.
So funny that both Carlas hold their tummy.

The Adventures of Carla Johnson

She always says, night then love I'll leave
your door open. I always sneak out of bed and close it.
Every step I take has to be as quiet as held-in breath.
I cannot afford a pin dropping, the shock of a sneeze.
So when I close the door, it takes me half an hour
to make it from my bed and back again.
So slow to avoid the cat's miaow of the door,
then it's tiptoe over the threadbare carpet.

When it's dark in my room my friend
Carla Johnson comes—she has wings
fabulous things, kiwi fruit and tangerines.
Come on Carla, she taps me on the shoulder.
We fly out the window, quiet as burglars.

We only fly to places with good names
that begin with the same letter of the alphabet.
On a single night we covered Alaska, Alabama
Albania; tonight is Louisiana Lithuania and Largs
because I went there when I was four
(strictly speaking, it is not a nice name).
Far from being tired in the morning
I feel quite rejuvenated—no jet lag whatsoever.

Mother's Castle

I don't know why I get so het up
about going to the seaside anymore,
because she always takes my bucket
and my spade and starts to dig like there's no
tomorrow. Making an absolutely massive castle.
Which at first with its turrets is fun.
But then, it just goes on and on.
The castle's got to have a moat.
The turrets need shells for decoration.
I've got to collect seaweed even—
and it smells. Sooner or later,
the whole beach has gathered to watch
her castle grow completely enormous, tall
as me. She doesn't even talk to anybody.
She's totally concentrated, all serious.

But, see when the sea comes and knocks it down.
See when the sea comes and the turrets crumble.
And the incoming tide washes over the castle's shells,
and they float backwards into the sea, honestly
that is the only time I ever see my mother crying.

Down at the very bottom

You can't see my castle. She can't either.
Nor can my big brother who is busy burying
his feet.

My castle is underneath the sand, down
at the very bottom of the sea, where
the other Carla is having her tea.

There are no big things at the side going boom.
And inside there's lots and lots of room.
So we don't get on top of each other.

Also, there are secret passages that lead to
terrapins, sea urchins, sea dragons and snakes
and if you turn right at the very bottom,

you can even go back in time; you might run into
a tyrannosaurus Rex or some kid in period dress.
The sleeping room is turquoise at first, then

all of a sudden, it goes dark green. But the best
thing is that nobody says, 'if you don't . . . then you
can't . . .'
Nobody talks like that in my castle under the sand.

Waves

There are waves to chase and waves that crash,
There are waves to jump like skipping ropes,
Waves to run away to sand, waves to leap and bound.
Waves that are turquoise, waves that are brown,
Waves full of seaweed, waves that drown.
Waves clear and calm, waves angry and wronged,
Waves that whisper, waves that roar like thunder,
Waves you'd never swim under, pounding rocks and
  shore.

Waves that put you to sleep, sssh sssh sssh cradle-rock.
Waves that look like sea horses or sheep or curly froth.
Waves that are cold as bare floor, waves that are warm as toast.
There are waves called the Black Sea, the Red Sea, the North Sea,
Waves called the Pacific ocean, the Atlantic ocean, the Antarctic.
If you counted them all, wave upon wave upon wave
would it be a hundred, a thousand, a billion—or more?

The Black Sea

After John Macpherson drowned
I walked the Black Sea coast with Annie.
During the day we'd stand
at the very same spot and she'd say
John, Johnnie into the Black Sea
and other things I didn't understand.
It was only with me she talked to him.
I'd see the sea frothing out his mouth
the day my father tried to save him.
Six days Annie waited in that hotel
for an aeroplane that would take him
back to Glasgow, for a Catholic burial.
Six days in 84 degrees fahrenheit;
Annie behind the wooden shutters mostly,
listening to the thud of the volleyball
hit the courtyard again and again.

Two Niagaras

Whilst I was doing the dinner dishes
Carla Johnson flew past the moon
twice, in different skies,
and landed in Toronto five hours behind
the Greenwich Mean Time. Autumn.

All rust and yellow and glowing orange.
Trees ahead of ours, lit like halloween lanterns.

So she said anyway.
Sometimes I think she lies.

Her wings were tired on the Wednesday.
A long long day till night. She drank pints
of water to escape jet lag. Ate three
blueberry muffins. And slept while
I was having my branflakes and raisins.

Next day she thought she'd give her wings
a wee break, so she takes the bus to Niagara.

So she said anyway.
Sometimes I think she lies.

She said the American side was on the left
and small and the Canadian side was on the right
and huge and had a luminous green light at the top.
In the sky was the biggest rainbow ever.
She went on the Maid of the Mist Boat.

She wore a blue raincoat.
The fall soaks you, you get absolutely soaked.

That's what she said anyway.
But sometimes I think she lies.

Right under the right side of Niagara
there was a stink of a mist
like somebody was furious.
Children get lost in that mist
You can hear their cries falling,

Calling Carla, pick me up and carry me off.
It was sad, kids crying like that.

But you know Carla she's a born liar.
She makes things up. A right wee fibber.

A pinocchio. Always crying wolf or fire.
But then again, so do I. Occasionally. No I don't.

On the road back from Phalassarna

My mum doesn't stop talking:
'There's an old woman dressed in black
carrying lots of leaves on her back
—or maybe it's parsley. There's a man on a donkey.
Look. There's some mountain goats with bells
round their necks and long beards.
Oh I know it's a long journey.
We'll soon be home. Look the sky is pink.'
I want another donkey, I say. *Too much talk.*
'Maybe. Look at the drop down, those mountains.
Look, there's another goat.' *But I want a donkey*
I say, again, and again she says, 'Maybe. There's a
tractor.
Oh look Matthew look here's a donkey pulling a goat.'
Where where I say and she says, 'Did you miss it?'
I missed the donkey, I cry, *I don't believe it.*
'It is late. Don't do that. We need to concentrate.
We're coming in to Chania. Watch out for signs.'
I want another donkey. 'Sssssssh.
Look at the traffic lights, the bright tavernas.
The people out at night. Look there's a fight.
Sssssh, sssssssh. Forget your stupid donkey.'

Kalives, Crete

Matthew says the men at Kalives Square,
(the men with the wrinkles who drink beer,
or tiny cups of coffee and say Kalimera
which Matthew pronounces Can of Beera)
play snap.

These men are the same men who show
Matthew their kittens which are all called
Kalimera as well by Matthew. Four Kalimeras
and one Mama. The same men who show him hens
squawking,

or walking on ginger feet. Or rabbits or cockerel.
These are the men with palms full of walnuts
or chocolate cake. They pat Matthew's head and
  laugh.
Kalimera. Kalispera. Kalimera. Kalispera
up the steep hill.

Eating out in Kalives

In the tavernas at night for our feta
(which is better than cheddar) and my chicken pie,
there are so many tiny kittens which I
feed with chicken from my chicken pie
(I only like the pastry).

Round the same table in the square are
the old men playing snap and a dog
that wants to play snap too, on my ankles.
So my feet are on the table with the olive oil
and it keeps well off.

But this is it though, eating out, outside.
When I get back, we will be back to the kitchen table
the vegetarian sausages, and the pasta bake.
But here on holiday I am up late and there's
the tiny kitten, the Greek stars.

Hairpin Bend

Around the hairpin
bends
where the drop
down
gives you vertigo
and
you cling
to the steering wheel,
there are
mountain goats
who
ring their bells
while
you get dizzy
and even
dizzier,
they are just happy—
long beards
shaking—
probably
laughing
a goat's guffaw
at the tourist's
silly fear of heights.

Aaaargh. Help.

Big brother's Big Catch

On the tiny rowing boat my brother disgusted me
hammering his great catch with a massive mallet
almost maliciously, his eyes glinted when ages
later the bloody fish started to jump again.
What did he call that? Not afterlife, something
clinical. It jumped across the cupped hands
of the boat like the flat stones he was so good
at skitting. The saliva started to make my
jaw quiver till I threw up into one wave after another
only to have my brother accuse me of poisoning them!

It didn't end there. There was the mean smile
of the sharpened knife ripping the rainbow skin
till orange eggs fell out like extra-terrestrials.
Then, the dead yellow teeth hanging out a ruined
  mouth;
the bulbous, spongy eyes. Who could eat with them
watching? At night I dreamt of them coming out
of people's mouths whole, undermining everything
they had to say. A whole pike on the Wilton carpet.

Once he offered me his spare rod like a peace treaty
after some fight. He baited it with luminous maggots
and we waited in that special fisherman's silence
for ages, until eventually and all of a sudden something
pulled on my rod. The fear tugged like some bad
memory.
Could I pull it out? Prove myself? Or maybe it would
leap
from my mouth when I was talking to my best friend.
I couldn't. I screamed *something's there* and gave him
the line.
Like a typical girl. I disappointed myself; the biggest
yet
came struggling up the air on the rope, still hoping to
escape.

Sheep Shearing, Skye

I park outside the pen.
They are all jostling and shoving
panicking really panicking; the fear,
I can smell it stronger than ferns
or seaweed. *On you go before me*
That's what it's like. Really pushing
each other about. Out for themselves.

You point at the old man with the bunnet ,
and the young one with his floppy curls—
I could see them cut. The whole lot. See how
he'd like it. Let me try that on you son.
They each take one: hooves on tiptoe.
Neck way back. Arms round like a noose.
That high strangled sound; *save me.*

My wee boy cries like a lamb. Can't stand it.
The constant clip clip clip and all that wool
falling to the ground, falling like snow. Years ago
I remember my dad saved one from barbed wire.
Its hind legs strong frantic kick when it ran off.
I walk on down the road; bracken on one side
the sea below the other. The buggy gets caught

In a cattle grid. You laugh. I'm caught
too. And the midges will be out soon.
I've got no lavender to keep them off.
But nothing beats them anyway. It's whole gangs
of them you have to deal with. And, suddenly;
most of them are done. All bald and spindly.
Fragile like another animal was hiding underneath

All that time, like a convict. Look. Look.
You point at the barenaked creatures.
All their loot lying on the ground. Look.
Yes, it will grow back, honest it will.
Though right now, it is unimaginable.
The old man and the young one wave hello.
'Whose they' you say. 'Whose those men?'

bunnet = cap

Pumpkin for Maxine

On Hallowe'en Mum and I made a pumpkin lantern;
huge triangular eyes and a square nose.
It cried when we dug out its pyramid teeth:
Ouch, it said, *this is worse than the dentist.*
I got a fright; but the strangest thing was,
my mum didn't hear it. *Dentists at least give gas,*
Pumpkin complained. There was my mum, oblivious,
still hacking out its brain. 'Come on. Dig in,' she says,
'this is taking hours; it'll turn back into a carriage.'
I started feeling dizzy, giddy, all out of sorts.
I tried to hold its jaw closed so it couldn't talk.
Ouch, it said, *my cheekbone; do I have to be hollow?*
'Of course you do,' I whispered, 'this is all hallow's
eve. We will put a candle in the hollow.' *Oh No,*
screamed Pumpkin. *I'm going to burn, my skull.*
Worse than Catherine. Suddenly, Pumpkin rolled
off the table. 'Look what you've done!' shouted Mum.
'You careless thing.' 'It wasn't me,' I said breathless,
and pleased. Pumpkin was trying to escape.
'Oh, for goodness sake,' said Mum.
'What's the matter with your head?'
It's not her head, Pumpkin said, *It's mine.*
I've got a dreadful headache, got anything for it?
But, my mum, who'd suddenly, finally heard it—
Pumpkin's piercing voice—fainted, falling
into the basin with all the apples for the dooking.

The Monster with two Mouths

One day I was on my travels, having a bit of a kip,
when I heard this shuffle shuffle noise, looked up
and to my surprise I saw a monster with four lips.
In other words, two mouths. I says 'hello,' being
polite.
She laughs out one mouth. *Are you talking to me?*
pleased.
'Can you see anybody else about?' She looks around.
She has four eyes, green, yellow, blue and brown.
Quite fetching really. Like one of those changing pens.
Or a rainbow. I tell her this—'I'm calling you Rainbow
Eyes.'
She cries out the other mouth. *That's awful nice.*
'Well, why are you crying then?' I ask. *Because.*
Sometimes
when things are awful nice I get so happy I could sob,
honestly.
You know, soak my six pillows. 'I know' I says (privately
thinking my mum is scrimping on the pillowline. I
have one.)
'So, Rainbow Eyes. Would you like to ride my bike.'
I'm too big she says out her sad mouth. 'Karata.
Karata.
Karata,'

I says and there she is tiny, toty. Smaller than me.
Hops on my bike and is off, *'wheeeeee.'* 'Hey you,'
I says chasing her. Puffing. My heart going faster
than my new trainers. She brakes. *That was sharp.*
'Baramba Baramba' I make her bigger. *What's your*
name?
'Carla. Call me Carla.'

I'm Not Old Enough Yet

Even at three, this business of a big man
coming down the chimney loaded with pressies
from your list (who showed it to him?
Why wasn't he covered in soot?) seemed a bit far-
fetched.
Especially since we didn't have a chimney.
But later I started to believe in this man
with the beard longer than God's.
I left food out. I tried to stay awake.
I still suspected Santa was a black woman dressed in
red,
but I never, since three, asked my mum any questions.
Now I'm seven. A pal of mine asks, 'Do you believe
in Santa Claus?' *What do you mean*? 'Do you think it's
true,'
she continued until my mouth fell open and I started
to scream:
You shouldn't have told me. I'm not old enough yet.

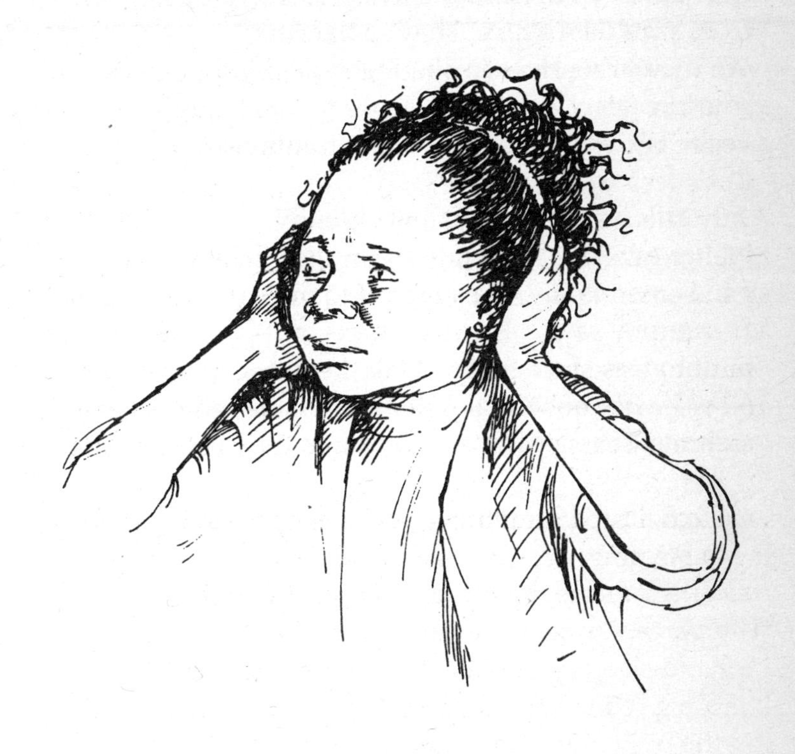

Hogmanay for Matthew

Funny. Nobody tells me to go back to sleep.
I hear loud voices from the living room.
We bump down stairs. They're dancing
with their arms crossed singing something
about my deer, my deer. I dance too and laugh
a really big laugh that makes my tummy sore.

Andy falls asleep on the floor. Wendy
and her two Dutch friends are in the kitchen
sink. Someone says they are off to my cot.
My mummy says, 'just sleep here' and pats the carpet.
I'm not pleased. It is silly. I tell them it is rude
and silly. But nobody is listening. Just laughing,
laughing. Tears even running down their cheeks.

I try and sleep. Something tickles my cheek.
It is a big ginger cat. *I've come for the party.*
Any food left says the cat, *any chance of a drink.*
'The party's gone. Go away. Shooo I say.'
I try and sleep again when something licks my arm.
It is a big red setter. *Hey you* it says to me since
I'm the only one with my eyes open. 'What do you
want?'

The party woof, it says, *the party woof*. 'Get lost' I say.
I have bad manners I know, but I want to go to sleep.
It starts to lick my toes. It tickles. 'Ok then,' I weave
my way through all the sleeping big people till I find
the dog some black bun, some shortbread, some Iron
bru.
Then the dog falls asleep. Suddenly. At my feet.

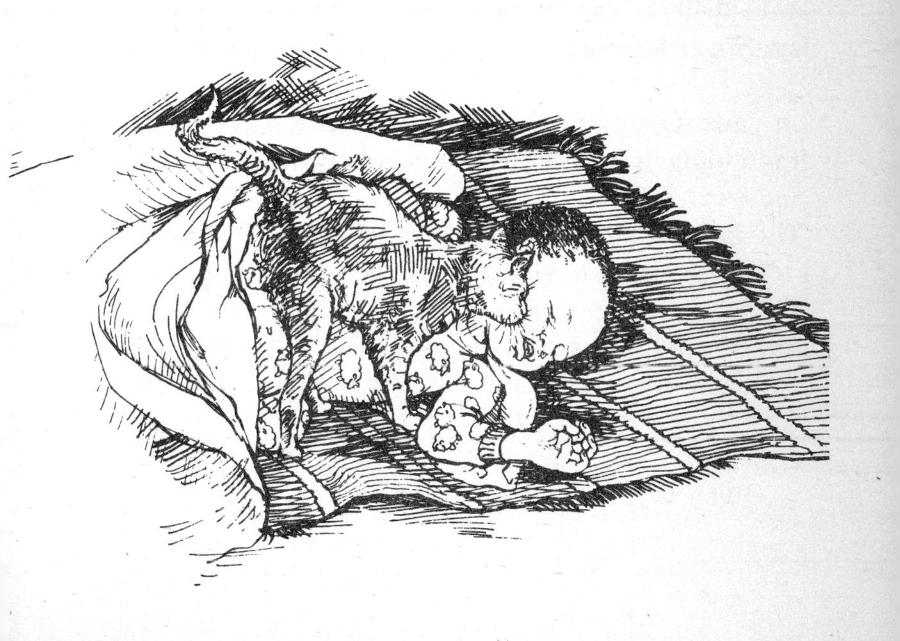

Burns Supper

The big night was bigger than Christmas
so it was, neeps and haggis

to fill your belly. The day,
the 25th of January, Burns's birthday.

A red trouser suit is what I was wearing,
bellbottoms, platform shoes, stalking

my way around the big room like a flamingo,
squeeling, hello, hello

to all the people at the Yoker Branch supper,
Patrick Burgh (lesser) hall. Jack does the immortal:

we remember Burns was only 37 when he died
poor, that he was an honest man who never lied.

But Rabbie, see this, all us singing 'Ae Fond Kiss'.
Centuries of 'Auld Lang Syne'. Imagine this.

The haggis, piped in like a glowing bride.
The bagpipes bellowing till it swells with pride.

Then there's the address To a haggis:
'Fair fa' your honest sonsie face . . .'

Pooer haggis—'Great chieftain of the Pudding Race'
I'm sorry for it but I'm enjoying the spice, the taste.

Anna sings my favourite song, 'John Anderson, my jo.'
Jessie reads a funny poem, 'Willie Wastle'. I know

Rabbie Burns is peering through the window
of Patrick Burgh (lesser) hall. The lights low.

Like Tam O'Shanter he's standing on the outside.
Suddenly I want on. I want to perform. I slide

off my chair, jump onto the long trestle table
and shout as loud as I am able,

'Weel done, Cutty-sark!
And in an instant all is dark.'

Alec shouts, 'Jesus! That gave me a fright.
Quick someone! Turn on the lights.'

Now the room is full of big laughs and lassies.
Tam's spirit and a toast to the laddies.

I pretend I'm giving the speech, holding my stem
glass,
miming the words in my red bellbottoms. I've got
class.

Skelf Helpline

Another one for Carla Johnson I say to myself
(I like using my whole name). Another skelf.
This girl is two and three quarters, Yomi.
She says she did it to herself only yesterday;
but that could mean two weeks or something,
all the little little ones get mixed up with time.

When I get there, (which was a bit of bother
—her house wasn't on the street finder).
She is standing outside it, (2 up-2 down) greeting,
Holding her thumb saying, *it's still hurting*.
'Awright. Awright. Let's have a decko.' *Ouch*,
she says, *Ouch. Ouch*. 'You're a brave wee thing,'

I says, trying some of my skelf patter. 'Hang on.
We won't be another minute. Where's my tweezers?
Oh, you've got a big one there dear.' I pinch and pull.
Ouch. It's awful sore, says Yomi, *awful sore*.
And out it comes, suddenly. Flies out, a wooden bird.
Soaring. I slap it in the air. 'Want to see what caused

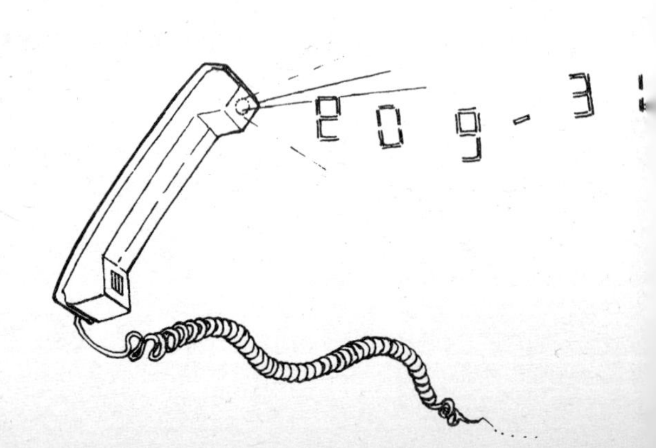

All that bother?' *No I don't* says she, sniffing.
Get rid of it. 'Oh no, I can't possibly do that,
I says. 'This skelf's going into my collection.
Rescue number 404. Now, a couple of questions:
How did you get it?' *I was trying to put on a CD,*
says Yomi. *My mum's top shelf. Almost reached PLAY.*

'Oh well,' I says. 'There you go. Got your message.
Don't meddle with your mammy's toys.
She probably put that skelf there for you, you know,
To teach you. What do you mean you don't believe
  that?
You should hear some of my stories.' *Bleep Bleep.*
  'Hello? Yes, your address?
. . . That's my skelf line. Cheerio.'

Skelf is Scottish for splinter.

0-861536 - HELP - HEL

English Cousin Comes to Scotland

See when my English cousin comes,
it's so embarrassing so it is, so it is.
I have to explain everything
I mean Every Thing, so I do, so I do.
I told her, 'know what happened to me?
I got skelped, because I screamed when a skelf
went into my pinky finger: OUCH, loud.
And ma ma dropped her best bit of china.
It wis sore, so it wis, so it wis.
I was scunnert being skelped
when I wis already sore.
So I ran and ran, holding
my pinky, through the park,
over the burn, up the hill.
I was knackered and I fell
into the mud and went home
mocket and got skelped again.
So I locked myself in the cludgie
and cried, so I did, so I did,
pulling the long roll of paper
onto the floor. Like that dug Andrex.'
Whilst I'm saying this, my English cousin
has her mouth open. Glaikit.
Stupit. So she is, so she is.
I says, 'I'm going to have to learn you
what's what.' And at that the wee git
cheers up; the wee toffee nose says,
'not learn you, teach you,' like she's scored.

skelped = spanked mocket = filthy
pinky = finger cludgie = toilet dug = dog

Sassenachs

Me and my best pal (well, she was
till a minute ago)— are off to London.
First trip on an inter-city alone.
When we got on we were the same
kind of excited—jigging on our seats,
staring at everyone. But then,
I remembered I was to be sophisticated.
So when Jenny starts shouting,
'Look at that the land's flat already'
when we are just outside Glasgow
(Motherwell actually) I feel myself flush.
Or even worse, 'Sassenach country!
Wey Hey Hey.' The tartan tammy
sitting proudly on top of her pony;
the tartan scarf swinging like a tail.
The nose pressed to the window.
'England's not so beautiful, is it?'
And we haven't even crossed the border!
And the train's jazzy beat joins her:
Sassenachs sassenachs here we come.
Sassenachs sassenachs Rum Tum Tum
Sassenachs sassenachs how do you do.
SASSENACHS SASSENACHS WE'LL GET YOU!

Then she loses momentum, so out come
the egg mayonnaise sandwiches and
the big bottle of bru. 'My ma's done us proud,'
says Jenny, digging in, munching loud.
The whole train is an egg and I'm inside it.
I try and remain calm; Jenny starts it again,
Sassenachs sassenachs Rum Tum Tum.

Finally we get there: London, Euston;
and the very first person on the platform
gets asked—'are you a genuine sassenach?'
I want to die, but instead I say, *'Jenny!'*
He replies in that English way—
'I beg your pardon,' and Jenny screams,
'Did you hear that Voice?'
And we both die laughing, clutching
our stomachs at Euston station.

Sassenachs is a Scottish word for the English.

Moving Country

Uncle Andrew's camera is on the table.
I am underneath the checked cover.
His shiny shoes walk out the door.
I grab his camera and run under
our house. Our house is on stilts.
All my secrets lie underneath.
My torch lights up my big blue box.
I run down the market, click
Mrs Joseph and her fish, click
my pal Frances, click the banana woman.

Suddenly we move to England.
Uncle Andrew takes our picture by the boat.
We wave and wave till he is a tiny dot.
At school they say, Where are you from?
Where are you from? Mimick my accent.
Rubber lips, they say. Chocolate Drop.
At night I twist my hair tight, tight.
Tell myself that my blue box is still there.
Write my friends a letter that starts,
'Here I am, my new school is brilliant.'

Latch Key

My best friend Danny comes to dinner with a key
round his neck, tied on with a piece of string.
At night when no one's home he lets himself in,
even though he is only seven, only seven.
My mum says he's too young and it's a shame.
He watches TV alone and eats crisps left for him.
And Mrs Robinson—the old woman next door—
listens out for him. Though my mum says,
she is hard of hearing. What does that mean?
Danny's mummy is always rushing off somewhere,
all dressed up to the nines and sometimes,
when the taxi comes she throws a kiss
like a piece of bread to a duck; it drops on our street
with a sigh. Then Danny scoops up his kiss
and comes into our house holding on to it.
Can Danny have a bath with me? I plead,
and my mum sighs yes, she supposes so,
because he is only seven, only seven.

Duncan Gets Expelled

There are three big boys from primary seven
who wait at the main school gate with stones
in their teeth and names in their pockets.
Every day the three big boys are waiting.
'There she is. Into her boys. Hey Sambo.'

I dread the bell ringing, and the walk home.
My best friend is scared of them and runs off.
Some days they shove a mud pie into my mouth.
'That's what you should eat,' and make me eat it.
Then they all look in my mouth, prodding a stick.

I'm always hoping we get detention.
I'd love to write 'I will be better' 400 times.
The things I do? I pull Agnes MacNamara's hair.
Or put a ruler under Rhona's bum and ping it back
till she screams; or I make myself sick in the toilet.

Until the day the headmaster pulls me out,
asking all about the three big boys.
I'm scared to open my mouth.
But he says, 'you can tell me, is it true?'
So out it comes, making me eat the mud pies.

Two of them got lines for the whole of May.
But he got expelled, that Duncan MacKay.

Lovesick

I'm scared of my own heart beat;
it's so loud someone might say
'who's on the drums?' and I'd blush
(not exactly beetroot) but blush
all the same.

I have these feelings.
I take them home from school
and tuck them up. In the morning
I say all the wrong things by accident
again and again.

Like, for instance, shouting *Miss*
in the middle of someone else saying
something. Usually Agnes MacNamara.
'In a minute,' says Miss. And I blush.
I hate MacNamara.

Miss is from Bangladesh and has
thick black hair, usually brushed
into one sleek pony. If I could tie the bow!
She has lovely eyes, dark pools.
Miss isn't married.

But I expect she will get married soon.
I think Mr Hudson wants to marry her.
Mr Hudson is always waiting in the corridor.
Him or that Agnes MacNamara.
Will I ever. Will I ever

Get older so that it doesn't hurt.
So that my heart doesn't hurt.
So that I don't spend all my time
with my fingers crossed and wishing:
Say something nice. Miss, Please. *Something*.

Carla's Kisses

Carla Johnson doesn't need an air balloon
to go from Sri Lanka to Siberia.
She doesn't need a magic carpet
to visit her grandmother in Nigeria.
She doesn't need a space rocket
to call on her aunt in her capsule in Mars.
Or an old fashioned tram to go back in time.

Carla Johnson doesn't need a submarine
to visit her pal the sea urchin.
Or a helicopter to see clouds first gather.
She doesn't need a steam train
to go from Burma to Belize.
She believes, all she needs, she believes

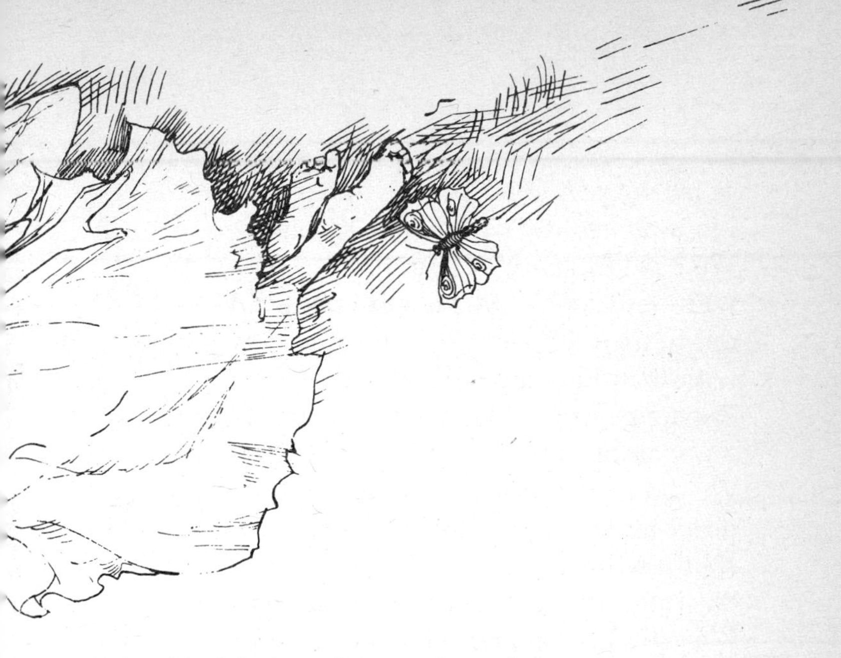

Is her kiwi fruit and tangerine wings,
a glass of water, before and after,
and a small fruit of the season—maybe
a mango, a black fig or a papaya.
Perhaps a pineapple, a paw paw or a banana.
Then she says: 'manana, manana, manana

I will fly to Morocco and then to Malaysia
Then up to Iceland' where her Innuit mate
always says, 'where have you been Carla,
so long!' and Carla smiles wide as her wings
because best of all Carla likes being missed.
So she says: 'Aw come on, not that long,' and gives a
kiss.
Carla's kisses taste of apricots or peaches or bliss.

Tomorrow they'll be coming to get me

This isn't paranoia. This is experience.
I've watched my pals go one by one.
We used to dance all together
with our friends that have been moved
out of their homes. Now new ones have come
with their long faces. White faces.
We are getting done in for a pound of beef
a wardrobe, a letter, a roll of toilet paper.
We did mount protests. Sit-in-the-forest-
don't-budge kind of thing. But we're no match
for those big machetes. They don't care.
Basically. We're not Burnham Woods either.
We can't just up and off to a nicer spot.
Then again, we've been here hundreds of years.
Tomorrow it is another story. Chop. Tomorrow
after that, chop chop, and so it will go on
until we are all done. But then.
There will be floods like Noah never imagined.
Bright blinding lights. The earth's skin
burnt to tatters. Mark my words.
This is a dangerous game they're playing.

Oxleas Wood

I have adopted a tree
with my own pocket money.
It only cost me
a fiver for that oak tree—
it is older than a century.

They are trying to build a
motorway through this magic
mystery, this ancient wise wood.

Whose will is done?
Who will let them?

They are trying to build a motorway
through this magic mystery,
this ancient wise wood.

We will wait for the bulldozers to come.
We will all lie down.
We won't let our children be chopped down.
We will all lie down.
We are the children who won't let our children go.
We are the parents who must lie down.
To fight for the ozone layer, the future.
The bark, the leaf, the branch, the air.
We will not be moved.

Premonition
(for Jonathan)

This kind of thing happens to me all the time:
I dream my hamster has escaped and I wake up
and there it is, buried under a pile of washing.

Or I see my best Aunt in a dream,
where all her lovely thick hair has disappeared,
and the next thing is everyone whispering

in the living room with cups of sweet tea.
Or else my mum climbs a ladder in a nightmare
and falls off it, two weeks later, in real life.

I tell you it spooks me out. It is scary.
Then dreams make things happen, don't they?

Pollution

Only when everyone in West Green Road
has gone to sleep: when every Doberman
has stopped barking, every ghetto blaster
stopped blasting and all the tom cats
have stopped fighting, does she walk the street
under the yellow light of the streetlamps.

She wears a silver sweatshirt and a brand new
pair of trainers; the huge tongue licks her toes.
With her busy brush and her dustpan dan she goes
through mounds of wrappers and applecores,
cans and empty cartons of milk, banana skins
and bottle tops. Munch into the big mouth.

She is fast and furious and very fit.
The anger in her eyes is a brilliant torch.
Passing each shop she tries to make up
a rap, but the drains and sewers, *Drip drip*,
make her feel she's a born loser, *Rat tat*.
Tomorrow they'll still be drinking dirty water.

Phobia—the year of the mouse

I don't know where I got it from—
might have been my mum,
could have been her cousin John,
might have been a generation passed on.

It was like a bug or a rumour,
down one street, up another.

Some houses it was spiders, some snakes.
Some mice, some cats, some rats.
Some couldn't stand being inside,
some outside. Some hated pigeons, some bats.

I don't know where I got it from;
but when the mouse ran
from the fridge to the cooker,
I ran from the kitchen door

to the corner shop and stayed there,
till after supper. I lost interest in meals.
But the strange thing was the look
on my mum's face when I told her.

It was like a bug or a rumour
down one street, up another.

In fact my whole family lost weight.
We plotted. We laid traps. We stole cats.

We trembled. We shook. We sweated in sleep.
We didn't feel at all well.

We could think of nothing else in our house,
but how to get rid of that mouse.
Before we could say boo to a bat,
everyone else was borrowing cats.

Till finally we held a street chat,
and found out to our dismay that
these street mice didn't mind cats.
And never even looked at the traps.

What could we do? There was the mouse doctor
who promised to make us better
to let us sleep again and eat our dinner,
for the whole town had become much thinner.

It was like a bug or a rumour
down one street and up another.

You see, before long the mice took over.
And the people were out on the streets.
It was an incredibly tough year.
The people cold; the mice snug, under duvets.

And the doctor wasn't well either.
Nor the town planner, nor the bus driver.
The teacher or the actor or the social worker.
They all looked a bit peculiar.

It was like a bug or a rumour
down one street and up another.

It lasted an entire year until
we couldn't take any more.
And so, together, we said, Enough.
And conquered our fear.

Well, we did tip-toe back.
And we were holding big brooms.
And we did shout when we entered the rooms.
Look out! Watch it! You've had it!

And our hearts were still in our stomachs.
Thumping. And the smell of all of us sweating
was quite something. But there it was.
We got our homes back. Can't have everything.

Pit Bull

Our next-door neighbour has a pit bull terrier.
The postman is so scared he delivers
their letters to us. My mum is so curious
she steams them open first.
'Anyone who has a pit bull
deserves no privacy,' she says.

A letter comes from the Government,
saying it has to be put down.
'What is that?' I ask my mum.
'Good,' she says, jumping up and down.
'It means it's going to sleep forever.'
'Like a fairytale?' 'Just like a fairytale,' she says.

Ever since the day that dog tried to bite
its way through our fence and I was in the garden
licking my ice-cream, and my mum screamed
'Come in, quick, come in,' and picked me up.
Ever since then, she has not liked the Dobsons.
'Can we not get peace in our own home?'

That's what she's said, ever since then.
Peering out the window first before
she lets me play in the garden. Listening
at the wall to hear the pit bull munching
its raw steak (probably) she says. 'Listen to it.
The great beast.' At night, she says, it snores

So loud the walls shake, but I never hear it.
I think my mum's got it in for the pit bull
next door. I think if my mum could put it down
personally, she would. 'Can they not make up
their mind?' she says when the Government
can't decide what to do with ten thousand pit bulls.

She made up hers. We moved house. Now
there is the constant noise of Rottweilers
on either side. I think I preferred the pit bull.
Actually, I think its bark wasn't worse.
My mum's started putting circles round houses
in the newspaper again. I won't unpack my toys.

New Baby

My baby brother makes so much noise
that the Rottweiler next door
phoned up to complain.

My baby brother makes so much noise
that all the big green frogs
came out the drains.

My baby brother makes so much noise
that the rats and the mice
wore headphones.

My baby brother makes so much noise
that I can't ask my mum a question,
so much noise that sometimes

I think of sitting the cat on top of him
in his pretty little cot with all his teddies.
But even the cat is terrified of his cries.

So I have devised a plan. A soundproof room.
A telephone to talk to my mum.
A small lift to receive food and toys.

Thing is, it will cost a fortune.
The other thing is, the frogs have gone.
It's not bad now. Not that I like him or anything.

What Jenny Knows

'I didn't come out my mummy's tummy.
No I didn't,' I says to my pal Jenny.
But Jenny says, 'you must have.
How come?' And I replies,

'I just didn't. Get it. I didn't.'
'Everybody does' says Jenny,
who is fastly becoming an enemy.
'Rubbish,' I say. 'My mummy got me.

She picked me. She collected me.
I was in a supermarket,
on the shelf and she took me off it.'
'Nonsense,' says Jenny. 'Lies.'

'Are you calling me a liar?'
I'm getting angry. It's not funny.
'No, but you have a tendency'
(a word from her aunty, probably)

'To make things up.'
'Look. I'm speaking the Truth.'
I say, 'Cross my heart.'
'Don't hope to die,' shouts Jenny.

Awful superstitious, so she is.
'I'm adopted,' I says, 'adopted.'
'I know That!' says Jenny,
'But you still came out

Somebody's tummy. Somebody
had to have you. Didn't they?'
'Not my mummy. Not my mummy,' I says.
'Shut your face. Shut your face.'

Big Hole

My best friend Jenny Colquhoun has moved on.
She's gone to live in a posher part of town.
She left a big hole; an empty space next to my desk.
My hands hold themselves on the way to school.

But see in her new house she has a dining room,
a TV room—imagine a room just for watching!—
and her own bedroom. I stayed the night;
got lost on my way back from the bathroom.

I was there the day before her ninth birthday.
I was the special friend from the old school.
But when her new friends came they stared
till I thought I should check the mirror, as if

I had a big hole in my tights. 'What did *you*
get Jenny for her birthday? '*Anne of Green Gables*'
I said, burning under the wrong dress,
wanting the thick carpet to swallow me up.

'Have you always been that colour?' says the one
with the freckles. And a giggle spreads from room
to room till Jenny's beautiful red-haired mother
saves me: '*Anne of Green Gables*? A wonderful book.'

Brendon Gallacher (For my brother Maxie)

He was seven and I was six, my Brendon Gallacher.
He was Irish and I was Scottish, my Brendon
Gallacher.
His father was in prison; he was a cat burglar.
My father was a communist party full-time worker.
He had six brothers and I had one, my Brendon
Gallacher.

He would hold my hand and take me by the river
Where we'd talk all about his family being poor.
He'd get his mum out of Glasgow when he got older.
A wee holiday someplace nice. Some place far.
I'd tell my mum about my Brendon Gallacher

How his mum drank and his daddy was a cat burglar.
And she'd say, 'why not have him round to dinner?'
No, no, I'd say he's got big holes in his trousers.
I like meeting him by the burn in the open air.
Then one day after we'd been friends two years,

One day when it was pouring and I was indoors,
My mum says to me, 'I was talking to Mrs Moir
Who lives next door to your Brendon Gallacher
Didn't you say his address was 24 Novar?
She says there are no Gallachers at 24 Novar

There never have been any Gallachers next door.'
And he died then, my Brendon Gallacher,
Flat out on my bedroom floor, his spiky hair,
His impish grin, his funny flapping ear.
Oh Brendon. Oh my Brendon Gallacher.

Don't Forget That

The bed in one house is harder than the other.
When I'm in 63, I always leave my green jumper,
or my pencil case, or something else I need.
It gets quite annoying. One adult saying,
'Remember this,' and the other one saying,
'Don't forget that.'

My room in one house is smaller than the other.
When I'm in 22A I miss Michael Jackson on my wall.
But I suppose I can't have two Michael Jackson
posters.
The nights in 63 he talks in his American drawl. He
says 'Carla, how you doing girl?' Or even HE says,
'Don't forget that.'

I discuss the houses with the other Carla.
We do the regular polls, decide the pros and cons.
Which house has more ice-cream;
which house gives better dreams;
which house is the most clean, and which says most
often,
'Don't forget that.'

Carla and I both agree ice-cream is better in 63.
But then 22A is definitely more tidy.
We get more treats. And more 'quality time'
(I've heard the adults say) 'More like Quality Street!'
And my week wouldn't be the same unless somebody
kept saying,
'Don't forget that.'

Two of Everything

My friend Shola said to me that she said to her mum:
'It's not fair, Carla (that's me) has two of everything:

Carla has two bedrooms,
two sets of toys, two telephones,

two wardrobes, two door mats
two mummies, two cats

two water purifiers, two kitchens,
two environmentally friendly squeezies.'

My friend Shola said to me that she said to her mum:
'Why can't you and Dad get divorced?'

But the thing Shola doesn't even realise yet,
is that there are two of me.

Index of First Lines